THE GOD IN YOU BIBLE STUDY SERIES

RICH!
GOD MEETING
YOUR DEEPEST NEEDS

A Bible Study by

Churches Alive!

MINISTERING TO THE CHURCHES OF THE WORLD
600 Meridian Avenue, Suite 200
San Jose, California 95126-3427

Published by

NAVPRESS ◯

BRINGING TRUTH TO LIFE
NavPress Publishing Group
P.O. Box 35001, Colorado Springs, Colorado 80935

Cover illustration: Catherine Kanner

Scripture quotations are from the *Holy Bible:
New International Version* (NIV). Copyright
© 1973, 1978, 1984, International Bible Society. Used by permission of Zondervan Bible
Publishers.

Printed in the United States of America

14 15 16 17/99 98 97 96

*Because we share kindred aims for helping local churches fulfill Christ's
Great Commission to "go and make disciples," NavPress and Churches
Alive have joined efforts on certain strategic publishing projects that are
intended to bring effective disciplemaking resources into the service of
the local church.*

*For more than a decade, Churches Alive has teamed up with churches of
all denominations to establish vigorous disciplemaking ministries. At
the same time, NavPress has focused on publishing Bible studies, books,
and other resources that have grown out of The Navigators' fifty years of
disciplemaking experience.*

*Now, together, we're working to offer special products like this one that
are designed to stimulate a deeper, more fruitful commitment to Christ
in the local gatherings of His Church.*

The GOD IN YOU Bible Study Series *was written by Russ Korth, Ron
Wormser, Jr., and Ron Wormser, Sr., of Churches Alive. Many indi-
viduals from both Churches Alive and NavPress contributed greatly in
bringing this project to publication.*

Contents

About the Author

In your hand you have just one item of a *wide range* of discipling helps, authored and developed by Churches Alive with *one overall, church-centered, biblical concept* in mind: GROWING BY DISCIPLING!

Convinced that the local church is the heart of God's plan for the world, a number of Christian leaders joined in 1973 to form Churches Alive. They saw the need for someone to work hand-in-hand with local churches to help them develop fruitful discipleship ministries.

Today, the ministry of Churches Alive has grown to include personal consulting assistance to church leaders, a variety of discipleship books and materials, and training conferences for clergy and laypeople. These methods and materials have proven effective in churches large and small of over 45 denominations.

From their commitment and experience in church ministry, Churches Alive developed the Growing by Discipling plan to help you

- minister to people at their levels of maturity.
- equip people for ministry.
- generate mature leaders.
- perpetuate quality.
- balance growth and outreach.

Every part of Growing by Discipling works together in harmony to meet the diverse needs of people—from veteran church members to the newly awakened in Christ. This discipling approach allows you to integrate present fruitful ministries and create additional ones through the new leaders you develop.

This concept follows Christ's disciplemaking example by helping you to meet people at their points of need. Then, you help them build their dependence on God so they experience His love and power. Finally, you equip them to reach out to others in a loving, effective, and balanced ministry of evangelism and helping hands.

Headquartered in San Jose, California, with staff across the United States and in Europe, Churches Alive continues to expand its Ministry in North America and overseas.

Introduction

Jesus Christ made God in you possible. Through Him you became alive and began an intimate relationship with God. You have many benefits in this relationship—benefits that fully justify saying, "I'm rich because God meets my deepest needs."

In *Rich!* you will see how wealthy you are. Your needs will determine which of your riches is most meaningful to you. If you are in turmoil, you'll probably look forward to studying "Peace" or "Comfort." If guilt feelings are disturbing you, "Clear Conscience" will be meaningful.

The chapters in this book stand distinct from one another. Think of them as twelve bags of money from twelve different countries. During your life, you will visit all of these "countries" and will need the corresponding bag of riches. You will spend some of the "money" you gather through this book right away. And you will want to put some of these riches into savings for later needs.

HOW TO USE THIS BIBLE STUDY. This book leads you through a unique approach to making the Bible meaningful. In each chapter you will study one passage, not isolated verses, to explore some of the major themes of God's Word. In the process, you'll learn Bible study methods that will be useful for the rest of your life.

You will gain maximum benefit from this book by completing the questions about the study passage and then meeting with a group of people to discuss what you discovered in your study.

No doubt, your group could spend many weeks exploring the richness of just one of these Bible passages. But much greater profit accompanies a pace of one chapter each week. This stride guarantees sustained enthusiasm that will leave people wanting more.

The leader's guide designed for this series aids the group leader in launching and guiding the discussion. It provides help for using the series in a home-study group or a classroom setting.

HINTS TO ENHANCE YOUR EXPERIENCE. The translation used in writing this study is the *New International Version* (NIV) of the Bible. All quotations are from this translation.

Though written using the NIV, this workbook adapts readily to other Bible translations. In fact, it adds interest and variety in group discussions when people use different translations.

Your book includes space to answer each question. But some people choose to mark some of their answers in an inexpensive Bible. Creating a study Bible like this allows a person to benefit from notes and information year after year.

Above all, *use* the insight you gain. The truths of the Bible were not recorded to rest on dusty shelves. God designed them to live in the experiences of people. In preparing this series, the authors never intended merely to increase your intellectual knowledge of the Bible—but to help you put into action the tremendous resources available in Jesus Christ.

"God loves you . . . and everyone else has a wonderful plan for your life."

1.
Love

Study passage: 1 John 4:7-21

Focus: 1 John 4:10: This is love: not that we loved God, but that he loved us and sent his Son as an atoning sacrifice for our sins.

1 Thousands of songs, poems, and letters have been composed to say "I love you." To understand the highest love, a person must approach it from God's point of view. What does this passage say about God's love for you?

One person, after reading these verses, described God's love as "active—taking the first step" (verse 19). How would you describe God's love for you?

2 Knowing about God's love is more than a mental exercise. It affects you at every level of life. According to verse 16, "We know and rely on the love God has for us." Give an illustration of how you rely on God's love.

3 Knowing and appreciating God's love enables you to love others. According to the passage, what are some reasons why you should love others?

Verse	Reason

4 When people turn their reasons for loving others into the practice of loving others, they reveal their true natures.

What do you know about people who love others? (Verses 7,12,16)	What do you know about people who don't love others? (Verses 8,20)

What do these statements reveal about your relationship with God?

Why do you think you should *not* use these statements to evaluate other people?

5 Verse 18 says, "There is no fear in love. But perfect love drives out fear." Consider the context carefully and then tell what you think this statement means.

How can you apply the concept of verse 18 to your relationships with other people?

6 From your understanding of this passage, how is it possible for you to be a loving person?

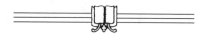

Jesus replied: "'Love the Lord your God with all your heart and with all your soul and with all your mind.' This is the first and greatest commandment. And the second is like it: 'Love your neighbor as yourself.'"

Jesus' reply to a Pharisee's question
Matthew 22:37-39

"... and whatever you do, Harry, don't demand to get everything that's coming to you!"

2.
Grace

Study passage: Ephesians 2:1-10

Focus: Ephesians 2:8-9: For it is by grace you have been saved, through faith—and this not from yourselves, it is the gift of God—not by works, so that no one can boast.

1 Our society says, "There's no free lunch!" That view makes the concept of God's grace difficult to understand. Yet, it is an essential ingredient in making possible your salvation. Use a dictionary to define grace.

With this definition in mind, list terms and phrases in the passage that you associate with grace.

2 The dictionary defines grace, but your experience helps you understand it. Read verses 1-3 and in your own words describe what you were like before you were made alive in Christ.

If you can remember, how did you feel about yourself then?

3 The grace of God through Jesus Christ has worked a change in you. In your own words, describe your life now, based on verses 4-10.

How does this make you feel about yourself now?

4 Explain why good works will not bring about the kind of life changes reflected in exercises 2 and 3.

Use the study passage to explain why good works are still very important.

5 Grace is important not only for salvation, but also for living the Christian life. According to the following verses, what is the role of grace in the Christian life?

	Role of grace
1 Corinthians 15:10	
2 Corinthians 9:8	
2 Corinthians 12:9	

6 Explain why you personally need God's grace

in your marriage or family.

in your church responsibilities.

in your work.

What gives you confidence that God's grace will help you? (If you don't have this confidence, what do you think will help you gain it?)

He giveth more grace when the burden grows greater,
He sendeth more strength when the labors increase;
To added affliction He addeth His mercy,
To multiplied trials His multiplied peace.

When we have exhausted our store of endurance,
When our strength has failed ere the day is half done,
When we reach the end of our hoarded resources,
Our Father's full giving is only begun.

His love has no limit, His grace has no measure,
His pow'r has no boundary known unto men;
For out of His infinite riches in Jesus
He giveth and giveth and giveth again!

Annie Johnson Flint
Hymn

3.
Peace

Study passage: Philippians 4:1-9

Focus: Philippians 4:6-7: Do not be anxious about anything, but in everything, by prayer and petition, with thanksgiving, present your requests to God. And the peace of God, which transcends all understanding, will guard your hearts and your minds in Christ Jesus.

1 The commands God gives you in this passage are designed to produce the peace you desire. List those commands.

When God tells you the result of obeying one of His commands, He is giving you a promise. In the study passage, what is promised?

---

2 Because God loves you, obeying His commands will help you enjoy life. In what way do you think the commands given in verses 4 and 5 can help you have peace?

Verse 4	Verse 5

---

3 It was necessary for Paul to urge Euodia and Syntyche to live in harmony (verses 2 and 3), indicating there was some tension between them. What suggestions would you make to people who are in conflict to help them live in peace? (Use ideas from the passage and your knowledge of other Scriptures.)

4 In John 14:27, Jesus speaks about peace. Read this verse. What do you think is the difference between how Jesus gives peace and how the world gives peace?

Does this verse indicate how you can receive Jesus' peace? Explain.

5 Imagine the following situation: You lose your job, use up your savings, and the bank is foreclosing on your house for lack of payment. Verse 6 of the study passage tells you to pray with thanksgiving. For what will you thank God?

What will be your request?

What do you expect to happen? (Verse 7)

6 Many times, two similar phrases are used in the same passage. For example, verse 7 contains *peace of God* and verse 9, *God of peace*. When you find a pair of phrases like this, it usually is helpful to identify the differences between them. Another pair of similar phrases appears in verse 7. What do you think is the difference between *guard your heart* and *guard your mind*?

Which of the phrases above is most important to you right now? Why?

7 Think of a time when you were experiencing anxiety. What did you need to change in your life in order to have the peace this passage talks about?

"I have told you these things, so that in me you may
have peace. In this world you will have trouble.
But take heart! I have overcome the world."

Jesus to His followers
John 16:33

"Of course we'll accept your check, but we'll need a driver's license, major credit card, your mother's middle name, a thumb print, blood sample and you'll have to leave your firstborn until the check clears."

4.
Acceptance

Study passage: Luke 15:11-32

Focus: Luke 15:24: For this son of mine was dead and is alive again; he was lost and is found.

1 Matthew states that Jesus "did not say anything to them without using a parable" (Matthew 13:34). The story in the study passage is one of Jesus' best known parables. To develop an overview of this story, briefly describe the main points.

2 Why do you think the father gave the young son his portion of the property?

3 The various actions of the young son show that he often changed his mind. What attitudes do you think are revealed by the son when he

a. asked for his portion?

d. decided to go home?

b. left home to live it up?

e. was greeted by his father?

c. took a job feeding pigs?

4 According to verse 17, the young man "came to his senses." In what way does a person who is not enjoying a close walk with God need to "come to his senses"?

5 How would you describe the father in this story? Be as complete as possible.

6 If the father in this story represents God and the prodigal son represents a person restored to fellowship with God, what kind of person does the other son represent?

What attitudes does this older brother reveal by

his refusal to join the party?

his reference to his brother as "your son"?

his statement, "I've been slaving for you and never disobeyed your orders"?

7 Most Christians have been wayward to some degree in their relationship with God. Will God always accept you if you want to return to Him? Explain.

If an unkempt and destitute person like the prodigal came to your worship service and said that he wanted to return to God, how would you respond?

---

8 The brothers in the story demonstrate certain strengths and weaknesses. Which of the two brothers are you most like?

What do you think you should do now to keep from experiencing the weaknesses of the brother with whom you most identify?

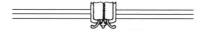

Lord, thank You for accepting me. I don't deserve it. I haven't earned it. But as a loving Father, You have accepted me into Your family. Please help me to accept and love others as You have done to me. Amen.

"It's for you, dear."

5.
Clear Conscience

Study passage: Hebrews 10:1-14 (included below)

Focus: Hebrews 10:14: Because by one sacrifice he has made perfect forever those who are being made holy.

¹The law is only a shadow of the good things that are coming—not the realities themselves. For this reason it can never, by the same sacrifices repeated endlessly year after year, make perfect those who draw near to worship. ²If it could, would they not have stopped being offered? For the worshipers would have been cleansed once for all, and would no longer have felt guilty for their sins. ³But those sacrifices are an annual reminder of sins, ⁴because it is impossible for the blood of bulls and goats to take away sins.

[5]Therefore, when Christ came into the world, he said:

> "Sacrifice and offering you did not desire,
>   but a body you prepared for me;
> [6]with burnt offerings and sin offerings
>   you were not pleased.
> [7]Then I said, 'Here I am — it is written about
>   me in the scroll —
> I have come to do your will, O God.'"

[8]First he said, "Sacrifices and offerings, burnt offerings and sin offerings you did not desire, nor were you pleased with them" (although the law required them to be made). [9]Then he said, "Here I am, I have come to do your will." He sets aside the first to establish the second. [10]And by that will, we have been made holy through the sacrifice of the body of Jesus Christ once for all.

[11]Day after day every priest stands and performs his religious duties; again and again he offers the same sacrifices, which can never take away sins. [12]But when this priest had offered for all time one sacrifice for sins, he sat down at the right hand of God. [13]Since that time he waits for his enemies to be made his footstool, [14]because by one sacrifice he has made perfect forever those who are being made holy. (Hebrews 10:1-14, NIV)

---

1 One reason the complete study passage is printed in your book is for you to mark some of your answers in the passage.

First, underline statements and phrases that refer to living under the law. Use another color to underline statements and phrases that refer to living in Christ. Now you can easily contrast the two concepts.

---

2 The underlining should help you complete the chart on page 26. Write what this passage teaches about sacrifice for sin, both under the law and in Jesus Christ.

SACRIFICE FOR SIN

	Under the law	In Christ
The frequency of the sacrifice	Verse 1	Verse 10
How it affects a person's conscience	Verse 3	Verse 2
Current status of sacrifice	Verse 9	Verse 9
God's attitude toward the sacrifice	Verses 5 and 8	Verses 7 and 9
Its power to cleanse	Verse 1	Verse 14

3 According to verse 1, the law is "a shadow of the good things that are coming." What is the relationship between an object (such as a tree) and its shadow?

How does this help you understand the relationship between the law and Christ?

4 In an attempt to gain a clear conscience, some people try to convince themselves that sins they have committed are really not wrong. Why do you think this attempt does not work?

26

How do you know this attempt does not please God?

5 If a person has the same attitude that Jesus Christ voiced in verse 9, do you think that person will have a clear conscience? Explain.

6 What problems are avoided (emotional, physical, and/or spiritual) when a person has a clear conscience?

According to the passage, if you don't have a clear conscience, what should you do?

Considering what you have learned in this study and in other passages, how can you *maintain* a clear conscience in Christ?

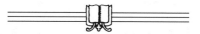

What God does with your sins

He removes them as far as the east is from the west.
He puts them behind His back.
He blots them out.
He remembers them no more.
He buries them in the sea.

So let your conscience be clear.

Psalm 103:12, Isaiah 38:17,
Isaiah 44:22, Jeremiah 31:34,
Micah 7:19

"But how did you accumulate this vast storehouse of knowledge?"

6.
Wisdom

Study passage: Proverbs 2

Focus: Proverbs 2:6: For the LORD gives wisdom, and from his mouth come knowledge and understanding.

1 When Solomon was anointed king of Israel, he made one request of God: "So give your servant a discerning heart" (1 Kings 3:9). God was pleased that Solomon made this request instead of asking for health, wealth, or victory. God responded, "I will do what you have asked. I will give you a wise and discerning heart, so that there will never have been anyone like you, nor will there ever be" (1 Kings 3:12).

This "wisest of men" wrote most of the Book of Proverbs, including the study passage. Before you begin studying the passage, write a short description of a wise person from your perspective.

2 According to verses 1-5, what do you need to do to gain wisdom?

What is one practical step you can take toward fulfilling one of the actions you listed above?

3 When you take steps to gain wisdom, you benefit in other ways, also. Wisdom never comes alone. According to verses 6-11, what other characteristics of life are associated with wisdom?

What is one reason you would like to have the above characteristics?

4 The passage teaches that "wisdom will save you" from two kinds of people. Complete the chart below based on verses 12-19 and your experience.

	Verses 12-15	Verses 16-19
The person from whom you are saved		
What this person usually seems to be		
What the person is really like		
Results of following this person		

5 Averting problems by being saved from the wrong people is one type of reward. What other rewards for living wisely are listed in the passage?

6 Using your understanding of the entire passage, evaluate the old saying, "Experience is the best teacher."

7 As a summary of your study, describe a wise person.

Compare the two descriptions you wrote for questions 1 and 7. What is the major difference between them?

He is no fool who surrenders that which he cannot keep to gain that which he cannot lose.

Jim Elliott, martyred for Christ
by the Auca Indians in Ecuador

"I think we made them too comfortable."

7.
Comfort

Study passage: 2 Corinthians 1:3-11

Focus: 2 Corinthians 1:3-4: Praise be to the God and Father of our Lord Jesus Christ, the Father of compassion and the God of all comfort, who comforts us in all our troubles, so that we can comfort those in any trouble with the comfort we ourselves have received from God.

---

1 The word *comfort* appears in the New Testament only twenty-four times. Its repeated use in this passage indicates it is part of the central theme. How many times does the word appear in the passage? (If you are marking a "study" Bible, underline every use of *comfort*.)

What words or phrases in the passage do you associate with discomfort?

Comfort can mean ease, as in a "life of comfort." What do you think it means in this passage?

2 Throughout the Bible various names of God are used. Often the name used emphasizes a particular characteristic of God. List the three names of God you find in verse 3. What does each name imply about His comfort for you?

3 Another name for God is Creator, indicating He is a God of purpose and design. According to the passage, what are some purposes for being comforted in difficulty?

Verse 4

Verse 6

Briefly describe an experience you have had that is similar to one of the following situations.

Situation 1
You were comforted during a difficult time, and this experience enabled you to comfort someone else who was having a similar difficulty.

Situation 2
You were comforted during a trial by someone who had gone through that difficulty previously.

4 Even though you may know that God has a purpose for your problems, it doesn't always keep you from experiencing emotional turmoil. What are some of the emotions Paul experienced when he had a problem in Asia? (Verses 8-11)

What are some emotions you have felt during a difficult time?

5 It was during this stress that Paul began to gain comfort. Answer the questions below using verses 8-11.

What did Paul do to gain comfort?

Why was he confident that God would comfort him?

What did the church do to help comfort him?

How can Paul's experience help you when you need comfort?

---

6 In 2 Corinthians 7:6-7 Paul describes another source of comfort. What comforted him?

Describe a similar experience in your life.

---

7 From what you have learned in this chapter, do you think it is better never to have had a problem, or to have had a problem and experienced God's comfort? Explain your answer.

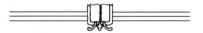

Lo, the great King of Kings, with healing in His wings,
To every captive soul a full deliverance brings;
And thru the vacant halls the song of triumph rings;
The Comforter has come!

Frank Bottome
Hymn

8.
Freedom

Study passage: Galatians 5:1-18

Focus: Galatians 5:1: It is for freedom that Christ has set us free. Stand firm, then, and do not let yourselves be burdened again by a yoke of slavery.

1 Green hills are more inviting from a prison cell. Opportunities become more attractive when oppression rules. Freedom becomes more precious whenever the horrors of slavery are visible. This passage contrasts living in freedom and living in slavery. In the chart on page 37, list words and phrases associated with these two concepts.

Living in freedom	Living in slavery
Verse 13—Love	*Verse 3—Obligated*

Look at your lists and give your opinion of one of the best aspects of freedom and one of the worst aspects of slavery.

2 The passage includes at least five major concepts: faith, love, justification, the Holy Spirit, and the law. Choose any two and tell how they are related to freedom.

Concept	How it relates to freedom

3 Pursuing the wrong goals can rob you of your freedom. In verses 2-6, Paul observed that some people were attempting to be justified by circumcision, the removal of the foreskin. A tradition among Jews, it was begun as a sign that God had made a covenant with Abraham and his descendants. To them, being uncircumcised meant being outside of God's care, provision, and guidance. The people who were attempting to be justified by circumcision became enslaved by it.

37

What are some ways that people today try to be justified apart from faith?

Explain why these ways also are forms of slavery.

---

4 Christ desires to give people freedom. But Paul says even Christ will be of no value to certain people. Who are they? (Verse 2)

Why will He be of no value? (Verses 3-6)

Explain how this principle applies to people today.

---

5 There is a contrast between obeying the law (verse 3) and obeying the truth (verse 7). From your understanding of the study passage, why does obedience to the law produce slavery and obedience to the truth produce freedom?

---

6 Though Christians have freedom in Christ, not everyone has used his freedom. Read verse 13 and give an example of using your freedom to serve someone.

Give an example of how someone might abuse the freedom Christ gives.

---

7 At the conclusion of all this teaching on freedom, Paul gives one command: "Live by the Spirit" (verse 16). What does this mean to you?

What is true about people who live by the Spirit?

What would you tell someone to do if he or she wanted to live by the Spirit?

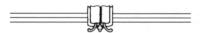

Jesus was talking to some Jews who became
believers in Him. He said, "If you live by the
principles I've taught, you prove to be My followers.
As a result you will know the truth and will be free."
They said, "We've never been enslaved by anyone.
Why do you say we'll be freed?"
Jesus answered, "The fact is, anyone who disobeys
Me becomes a slave to his disobedience. A slave
isn't a family member, but a child belongs to the
family. So if the Son sets you free, you're really free!"

John 8:31-36
a paraphrase

"Poor Solomon. He never seems to have anything decent to wear."

9.
Provision

Study passage: Matthew 6:19-34

Focus: Matthew 6:33: But seek first his kingdom and his righteousness, and all these things will be given to you as well.

1 The study passage is a part of the Sermon on the Mount, in which Jesus instructed His followers about how to live. List all the commands of the passage. Check those you think are the most important.

2 Jesus often used questions to make a point. Even though the replies may seem obvious, answering His questions will help you understand His reasoning.

Below are the verses in which Jesus asked questions. Next to each number, write your answer to the question.

25

26

27

28

30

What truth did this exercise emphasize to you?

3 Throughout the sermon, Jesus taught about God in down-to-earth terms. Instead of referring to Him as the One whose Name cannot be uttered (a Jewish tradition), He called God, "your Father." What does this name imply about God and His provision for you? (Verses 26 and 32)

Why might some people not want to think of God as a Father?

4 In this passage, Jesus makes two observations from
   nature and draws a conclusion after each one. Write these
observations and conclusions in the chart below.

Observations	Conclusions
Verse 26	Verse 26
Verse 28	Verses 29-30

5 Jesus noted that people in His day were concerned about
   food, drink, and clothing. What are some things people
are often anxious about today?

How do you know God cares about you in the areas you listed?

Choose one of the items you listed and tell what provision
the study passage indicates you should expect from God.

6 Asking several short questions about a verse will often help you understand it more completely. The following questions focus on verse 33. Write a short answer to each one. Most of your answers will come from your understanding, not the passage. Don't worry if they are not the same as other people's answers.

What does the word *first* mean in this context?

What does it mean to *seek His righteousness*?

To what does the phrase *these things* refer?

What is one thing that concerns you?

How does this verse help you recognize God's provision and not be anxious about this thing?

7 Seeking righteousness is a day-to-day process. Reread verses 27 and 34. In what ways do you think focusing on the future can keep you from seeking righteousness today?

8 Bill felt harried. An audit of his income tax revealed that he owed an additional $1089 to the government. The same day, he received a letter from a lawyer announcing the beginning of foreclosure proceedings. He was also mindful of the fact that his daughter would begin her sophomore year at a Christian college in three weeks. Bill found himself thinking, "More money would eliminate my worries."

What does the passage say that indicates God's provision does not always mean having more money?

What do you think you should do when you find you are thinking the same thing as Bill?

Aware of their discussion, Jesus asked them: "Why are you talking about having no bread? Do you still not see or understand? Are your hearts hardened? Do you have eyes but fail to see, and ears but fail to hear? And don't you remember? When I broke the five loaves for the five thousand, how many basketfuls of pieces did you pick up?"
"Twelve," they replied.
"And when I broke the seven loaves for the four thousand, how many basketfuls of pieces did you pick up?"
They answered, "Seven."
He said to them, "Do you still not understand?"

Jesus to the disciples
Mark 8:17-21

"O.K., we've decided that everyone whose last name begins with alpha to gamma will bring a main dish. . ."

10.
Family

Study passage: Acts 2:41-47

Focus: Acts 2:42: They devoted themselves to the apostles' teaching and to the fellowship, to the breaking of bread and to prayer.

---

1 Think of a family-like fellowship of about 120 people. They gather together, pray for each other, care for each other. Suddenly, their fellowship is inundated by 3,000 new people. Imagine their delight in the number of new believers. There is an explosion of enthusiasm. At the same time, being unprepared, ill-equipped, and semi-organized, they face the potential for misunderstanding and discontent.

With this in mind, what actions characterized the believers in this passage?

What attitudes do you think the believers had?

2 The word *love* is not used in the Book of Acts, but it is clearly demonstrated in this and many other passages. Describe at least three demonstrations of love found in this passage.

3 The 3,000 new people proved to be only the beginning of growth. According to verse 47, the church grew numerically every day. What do you think attracted people to this fellowship?

What do you think attracts people to a fellowship today?

What can you do to contribute to the things that attract people to your church?

4 The caring actions of these believers provide a challenge and an example, but not necessarily a rigid pattern. What are some problems that might develop if a church copied the example in verses 44 and 45?

What benefits would a church receive by following this example?

Give some reasons your church should follow the example in verses 44 and 45. Or, make an alternate suggestion to help meet the needs of people, and explain why your church should do it.

5 If newspapers, magazines, and television had existed, they would have sent reporters to cover the story of this fast-growing, highly-caring group.
   Imagine you are a reporter. Write a short news report about the church described in these verses.

6 Assuming the role of a reporter can be a useful tool when doing your Bible study. As in reporting, the cornerstone of good Bible study is making accurate observations. From these observations, you then draw conclusions and form applications.
   Perhaps the most difficult observation to make is noticing what is *not* there. For example, in this passage, there is no explanation of what the apostles taught. What are some

other things this passage does not reveal about the church it is describing?

When you think of the things that are recorded about this church (exercises 1 and 2) and the things that are not recorded, what conclusions do you make?

---

7 In what ways is your church like the church described in these verses?

How can you help your church become more like the church in Jerusalem?

We must realize that the most important single entity on this earth is God's kingdom manifested to the world, the church of Jesus Christ.[1]

Dr. Paul Y. Cho,
pastor of the largest church in the world,
the Central Gospel Church of Seoul, Korea

Note
1. Paul Y. Cho, *More Than Numbers* (Waco, Texas: Word Books, 1984), page 15.

"Good morning!"

11.
Courage

Study passage: Matthew 14:22-33

Focus: Matthew 14:27: But Jesus immediately said to them: "Take courage! It is I. Don't be afraid."

1 The crowds who followed Jesus learned from what He taught. But the disciples gained much more from the experiences they shared with Him. Next to each verse number below and on page 51, write a short statement that summarizes the *action* in the verse.

22

23 _____

24 _____

25 _____

26 _____

27 _____

28 _____

29 _____

30 _____

31 _____

32 _____

33 _____

2 There is no indication the disciples were afraid of the storm, but they did react in fear when they saw Jesus walking on the water. Why do you think they became fearful?

Which of these two (the storm or seeing someone walking on water) would most frighten you? Why?

---

3 Peter showed courage in getting out of the boat. He also experienced fear. Jesus said it was because Peter had little faith. In what did he place his faith in order to get out and walk on the water?

Where was his attention focused when he became afraid?

Why do you think Peter wavered in his faith?

What do you think he should have done when he wavered?

What should you do when your faith wavers?

What evidence can you offer that fear is the result of little or no faith? (Use ideas both from this passage and other Scriptures you know.)

---

4 After witnessing these events, the disciples concluded Jesus was the Son of God. How do you think this conclusion helped them to be courageous later in their ministry?

5 It is unlikely you will experience anything like these disciples did. But there are many other fears to overcome. Identify the fears you encounter.

☐ fear of failure   ☐ fear of the future

☐ fear of rejection   ☐ fear of death

☐ fear of financial disaster   ☐ fear of pain

☐ fear for children or grandchildren

☐ fear of _____

In what way has studying this passage helped you overcome your fears?

6 In obedience and daring courage, Peter left the security of the boat and took a step out into the storm. What do you think God would like you to do that requires a daring step of courage?

☐ Give more than I think I can afford.

☐ Tell my neighbor how God changed my life.

☐ Other:

Peter and John were seized and jailed by the same Jewish council that condemned Jesus to death. Refusing to back down, Peter proclaimed Jesus to be the Messiah. Acts 4:13 records, "When they [the council] saw the courage of Peter and John and realized that they were unschooled, ordinary men, they were astonished and they took note that these men had been with Jesus."

"Here's my plan . . ."

12.
Hope

Study passage: 1 Thessalonians 4:13–5:11

Focus: 1 Thessalonians 4:16-17: For the Lord himself will come down from heaven, with a loud command, with the voice of the archangel and with the trumpet call of God, and the dead in Christ will rise first. After that, we who are still alive and are left will be caught up with them in the clouds to meet the Lord in the air. And so we will be with the Lord forever.

1 Today, people often use the word *hope* to express wishful thinking, as in "I hope I win the contest." Others use the word *hope* to express their desire, such as "I hope you are feeling better." In Paul's vocabulary, *hope* meant a "future

certainty." Read through the passage and make a list of the hopes (future certainties) you have.

2 Based on the passage and your knowledge of other Scriptures, list some things that will happen at Christ's return that give you hope now.

According to the passage, why should you be convinced that Jesus Christ will return?

3 In 1 Thessalonians 5:2, Paul says the "day of the Lord" is like a "thief in the night." In verse 3, he says it is like "labor pains on a pregnant woman." Carefully read 1 Thessalonians 5:1-5 and complete the chart below.

	How this is like the day of the Lord	How this is unlike the day of the Lord
Thief in night		
Labor pains		

4 Those who look forward to the return of Christ are called "people of the day." In chapter 5, verses 4-11, they are contrasted to "people of the night." Compare these two kinds of people, using the chart below.

	People of the day	People of the night
What characterizes them?		
What is their future?		

5 Paul concludes his teachings about hope in 1 Thessalonians 4:18 and 5:11 with commands to the Thessalonian church. What commands use the phrases *each other* or *one another*?

What can you do to fulfill these commands in your church?

6 The main topic of this passage is the return of Jesus Christ. His return gives you the wealth of a prevailing hope. But this is not the only aspect of your riches mentioned in the passage. First Thessalonians 4:13 lists brothers, knowledge (not ignorance), and comfort (not grief). Continue to list as many riches as you can find in the passage.

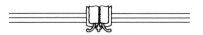

God has met your deepest needs. These riches should help you feel secure because you have what you need. And these riches grow as you spend them, rather than diminish.

Use your riches freely. Enjoy God's love, bask in His peace, accept His grace, comfort, and provision. Enjoying these riches benefits you and glorifies God.

Developing Lifelong Study Skills

The variety of methods you followed to complete the study are skills you can use throughout your life to understand and apply other passages in the Bible.

This summary identifies a few of the skills covered in this book, and will serve as a helpful guide for your future Bible study.

1. DETERMINING ATTITUDES. Many of the narratives in the Bible describe the actions of people without revealing their motives or attitudes. Often, attitudes are revealed (or at least indicated) by actions. For example, when you studied the parable of the prodigal son in chapter 4, you were asked what attitudes the son had during the events of the story. Considering his attitudes should have helped you gain new insights.

2. MARKING THE TEXT. In chapter 5, the entire study passage was printed in this book so you could mark it in any manner that helped you understand it. Underlining, arrows, circling, and noting questions and observations in the margin are a few of the many possible marks you can make. Some people prefer having an inexpensive Bible just for this purpose.

3. HISTORICAL CONTEXT. In chapter 8, one of the topics in the study passage was circumcision: "If you let yourselves be circumcised, Christ will be of no value to you at all" (Galatians 5:2). By looking at the historical context of circumcision as a Jewish rite of justification, you could interpret the statements properly.

4. ANSWERING QUESTIONS. Many passages use rhetorical questions to make a point. Answering them will often help you think through the argument and gain greater understanding. One example of using this technique is in chapter 9, where you wrote answers to six questions that Jesus asked.

5. OBSERVING (as a Reporter). The basis of all Bible study methods is the art of observing. The better your observations, the better your interpretations, your conclusions, and your applications. In chapter 10, you were told to describe this church through the eyes of a newspaper reporter. You also were to observe what was not present, one of the most difficult observations to make.